Cat Health and Wellness

FOR
DUMMIES®
A Wiley Brand

REVOLUTION Edition

FOR
DUMMIES®
A Wiley Brand

Cat Health and Wellness For Dummies, REVOLUTION Edition

Published by
John Wiley & Sons, Inc.
111 River St.
Hoboken, NJ 07030-5774
www.wiley.com

ISBN 978-1-119-01386-0

Printed in Singapore

10 9 8 7 6 5 4 3 2 1

Publisher's Acknowledgments

Project Editor: Tracy Barr

Acquisitions Editor: Erin Calligan Mooney

Editorial Manager: Rev Mengle

Business Development Representative: Susan Blessing

Art Coordinator: Alicia B. South

Project Coordinator: Erin Zeltner

Cover photo: Courtesy of Zoetis

Table of Contents

Introduction

Where your cat's health is concerned, one person makes all the difference in the world in how long and how well your pet lives. Want to guess who that one person is? The answer is *you*. You are the most important healthcare provider in your cat's life. *You* are the person who sees your cat every day, who feeds her, and who keeps her litter box clean. You are the one who knows where she likes to sleep and how much and how well she grooms herself. You are the expert on the sound of her voice, which toys are her favorites, and the way she likes to sit on the counter in the bathroom and watch you wash your face in the morning.

More than anyone else, you are the person who knows whether anything about your cat is a little off. Your powers of observation are the ones that keep her healthy — and maybe save her life.

From preventive care to making your cat's visits to the vet as stress-free and productive as possible, this book highlights all the ways you, working with your veterinarian, can help your cat live a long, happy, and healthy life.

This book was written on behalf of REVOLUTION (selamectin), a topical preventive that protects your cat from heartworm disease, fleas, and other parasites. For more information or to obtain the product for your cat, talk with your veterinarian.

Icons Used in This Book

This books includes icons that highlight certain kinds of information. Here's a rundown of what each icon means:

 This icon flags things that are especially useful for making life with your cat easier or for making your pet happier and healthier.

 When you see this icon, you've hit upon information that's worth reading more than once.

 Some things pose health or safety threats to your cat. This icon points them out.

Where to Go from Here

The information in this mini book is arranged so that you can easily find the information you're looking for. Simply thumb through until a topic catches your eye or head to the table of contents, where you can locate particular topics.

For example, if you're curious about preventative care for your cat, head to Chapter 2. Chapter 3 explains how to socialize your cat and teach her to enjoy car rides — two tasks that can reduce her anxiety during veterinary visits. Chapter 4 covers what you can do at the veterinary clinic itself to make those visits stress-free and productive.

Wherever you go in this mini book, you'll find information that helps you ensure your cat's well-being.

Chapter 1

Feline Health 101

. . . .

In This Chapter

▶ Understanding what's normal in your cat

▶ Recognizing signs that may indicate health problems

▶ Performing basic cat-care tasks

. . . .

You love your cat and know him better than anyone
else. Cats are very good at hiding signs of illness,
so you must try to be a keen observer to recognize
when something is wrong. The detective work starts
before you even suspect that your cat is ill and
includes a few of the same kinds of basic diagnostic
tools a veterinarian uses.

 Cats can live long, healthy lives. You can help
by making sure that your cat receives the benefits of preventive healthcare and is protected
from accidents and infectious diseases.

Recognizing the Signs of Good Health and Bad

To identify a potential health problem, you must be
able to recognize what is normal for your pet. Because
you know your cat better than anyone else, you're his

first line of defense. The key is to hone your instincts and then learn to trust them!

This section outlines the key health markers that you can observe to gauge your cat's overall health and alert you to potential problems that would benefit from a consultation with your veterinarian.

Health checks need to be regular to be useful. Your cat should be seen by your veterinarian regularly — at least annually. In addition, you should keep tabs on your cat with a monthly once-over that you perform yourself. This monthly check lets you can keep an eye out for potential problems before they become a threat to your cat's health. You don't have to make a big production out of this health check. Just incorporate it into a session that begins with petting and ends with your cat's favorite game — or more petting, if that's what he prefers.

Paying attention to general appearance

Stand back and look at your cat for a few minutes. Consider his posture, activity level, gait, coat, and over-all appearance for an impression of good health (see Figure 1-1). Note the following:

- ✓ **Is his body symmetrical?** Does the left paw look like the right paw? Is the right shoulder shaped the same as the left shoulder?

- ✓ **What is his demeanor?** Is he sluggish or lethargic? Does he lack "spring" in the step, or do you notice other, subtle signs you can't pin down and just sense that your cat's "not right"?

If something looks odd to you, be safe and ask your vet. She can tell you what's normal for cats and can advise you whether your cat needs to be examined.

Figure 1-1: Your cat's general appearance can give you an indication of his health.

©iStock.com/georgeolsson

Weighing in on weight

In general, most cats weigh anywhere from 8 to 12 pounds, but the range is very wide, depending on gender and breed. Really big cats, such as the Maine Coon, can be well over 15 pounds and be perfectly normal.

There are two things to pay attention to regarding your cat's weight:

✔ **Is it a healthy weight?** Your cat is in good condition if you can still feel his ribs when you pet him, but they are not sticking out. Too little or too much fat overall, as is the case with the cat shown in Figure 1-2, even if the weight remains constant, warrants a trip to the vet for weight management advice.

Figure 1-2: Carrying too much weight poses health risks for your cat.
©iStock.com/dennisvdw

To get a general idea of how much your cat weighs, here's a little trick: Step on the scale with your cat, note the weight, and then step back on alone. Subtract your weight from the total to get your cat's weight. Although this weight will be imprecise, it can at least tell you whether your cat is 10 pounds or 20 pounds.

✔ **Has your cat's weight changed abruptly or for no discernible reason?** If your cat loses or gains more than a half a pound — or less if the change is very abrupt — it's a cause for concern. Check in with your vet, who can run tests to determine the underlying reason for the change.

Cats are much smaller than humans are, so gaining or losing 1 pound in a cat that weighs 10 pounds amounts to a 10 percent change in body weight. If you were to lose 10 percent of your body weight — going from, say, 150 pounds to 135 pounds — in a week or two, it would be a reason to be examined by your doctor. Your cat is no different.

Examining the nose

A normal cat nose, as shown in Figure 1-3, can be either moist or dry but should definitely be clean, with no crusting or discharges. The nose pad should look pink, never white.

Looking at your cat's mouth

Take a peek at the mouth. Your cat may let you lift up his lips and look at his teeth. If he's very good, you may even be able to look inside his mouth. Pay attention to these things:

✔ **Teeth and gums:** Your cat's teeth should be clean and white, and the gums uniformly pink. Gums that are red and inflamed, pale, or blue are reason for concern. If the teeth are broken, missing, or loose, or if the gums have receded from the tooth and tartar buildup has discolored the tooth, then your kitty may have a dental problem that warrants examination by a vet.

Figure 1-3: A healthy cat's eyes should be bright and the nose free of discharge.
©iStock.com/deepblue4you

 Take a sniff. Your cat's breath may not smell like a rose, but it shouldn't be unpleasant or nasty. Bad smelling breath could indicate many things, from dental disease to kidney failure. Consult your veterinarian if you notice any unusual mouth odors.

 Cats get plaque on their teeth just like humans do. Plaque is a constant source of bacteria and leads to gingivitis (inflamed gums), which can make eating painful and serve as a source of bacteria for other parts of the body. Gingivitis can progress to gum disease (bone loss and receding gums). Left unchecked, gum disease can lead to tooth loss. Persistent plaque is a powerful source of bad breath.

- ✔ **Tongue and inside walls of the mouth:** Other signs that a trip to the vet is in order include a swollen tongue and lumps, bumps, or sores in the mouth. Dropping food when he eats, chewing only on one side of his mouth, drooling, or having any blood on his lips are likely signs of dental disease.

- ✔ **Spots in the mouth:** Some cats have dark spots in their mouths that are part of their own unique coloration. But some spots are abnormal. Get familiar with your kitty's mouth so you can detect changes, and if you notice any new spots, have your vet check them out as soon as possible.

Cats are very good at hiding when they hurt, and you may easily miss that they are in pain because of their teeth. Have your veterinarian examine your cat's mouth during his regular exams to make sure everything looks normal and healthy. Remember, most of the tooth is under the gum and in the bone. So only during your cat's teeth cleaning, when the vet takes x-rays, do you get to "see" the whole tooth and all of the bone.

Looking into your cat's eyes

The eyes should be clear and bright, and the pupils should be the same size. The following signs may indicate a health problem:

- ✔ Eyes that are dull or sunken, appear dry, or have thick discharge

- ✔ One or both eyes not centered between the lid or pupils of unequal size

✔ Whites of the eyes that are yellow, muddy brown, or bloodshot

Cats have three eyelids: the top lid, the bottom lid, and a third lid on the inside corner. You may see the third eyelid come up when your cat is sleepy, but it should not be visible all the time. If it is, that usually indicates your cat feels sickly (see Figure 1-4). Get him to the vet to check it out.

Paying attention to the ears

Look inside your cat's ears. They should be pink and clean. Healthy cat ears don't have any dark gunk or discharge, and they don't smell. A foul smell may indicate an infection. Other signs of ear problems include pain at the touch or your cat holding his head or ears in an unusual way.

If you see goo or something that looks like coffee grounds, your cat may have ear mites or an ear infection. Both are uncomfortable. With some

Figure 1-4: This poor kitty doesn't feel well. Notice the third eyelids.
©iStock.com/HAYKIRDI

simple tests, your veterinarian should be able to figure out what is wrong and prescribe medication to treat it, if necessary. Read all about these microscopic annoyances in Chapter 2.

Checking breathing and circulation

A cat that is breathing comfortably breathes almost silently; his chest wall moves easily in and out with each inhalation and exhalation; and his abdomen (stomach) barely moves at all. Signs that your cat may need a vet's attention include the following:

- ✔ Unusual noises (crackling and wheezing, for example) while he is breathing

- ✔ Breathing that is labored, rapid, or done with an open mouth

 Open mouth breathing in a cat is *never* normal. Consider it an extreme emergency and get him to a vet immediately.

- ✔ Breathing that excessively involves the abdomen

 One way to check your cat's circulatory system is to look at his gums or his tongue (this may not work in a cat with pigmented gums). Both the tongue and gums should be pink. Gums that are pale, white, red, or muddy looking may indicate a problem that needs to be checked out by your veterinarian.

Doing a hands-on check for lumps, bumps, and other stuff

 Be careful in checking over your cat because not all cats like being touched on their bellies or their feet. If your cat doesn't want you to look at his stomach, mouth, feet, or any other place, then respect his wishes. It's not worth stressing him out, nor is it worth you being bitten or scratched. Let your veterinarian be the one to examine those sensitive areas.

Inspecting the skin and coat

The skin is your cat's largest organ. Feel all over with your hands. Without getting rough, check for sensitive spots.

The skin should be clean, with no scabs, sores, pimples (yes, cats get acne), or missing patches of fur, which could be the result of ringworm (discussed in Chapter 2) or fleabite dermatitis.

Also examine your cat's coat (see Figure 1-5). Run a flea comb through the fur, looking for matting and flea dirt. A dull or clumpy-looking coat could be a symptom of a more serious health concern. Go to the later section "Taking care of your cat's coat" to find out what kind of grooming regimen your feline needs.

Peruse the paws, pads, and back end

During your exam, don't forget the paws. Make sure nothing is caught in your kitty's pads. Feel between the toes and pads for cuts or sores.

You may want to take this opportunity to trim your cat's nails. Head to the later section "Trimming your cat's nails" to find out how.

To check out your cat's rear, run your fingers all the way down your cat's tail to check for lumps or scabs. Now lift his tail and take a look. You don't want to see anything that looks like rice clinging to the fur — a telltale sign of tapeworms. (To find out more about tapeworms, look in Chapter 2.)

Figure 1-5: Examine your cat's coat for signs of matting and flea dirt.

©iStock.com/cynoclub

Taking Care of Kitty — the Basics

As a cat lover, you want to ensure that your feline stays healthy and comfortable. A large part of meeting that goal is to do general cat care: keeping his coat clean and well groomed, looking after his teeth, and trimming his nails. Taking care of your cat's coat, as well as his claws and teeth, keeps him healthier, makes him easier to live with, and strengthens the bond between you.

14

Cleaning your feline's canines

Ensuring healthy teeth and gums for your pet is one area where you and your veterinarian must work together. Regular cleanings under anesthesia by a vet are essential to ensure dental health (see Figure 1-6). In between these cleanings, you can do your part to take good care of your cat's teeth by using special toothpaste at home.

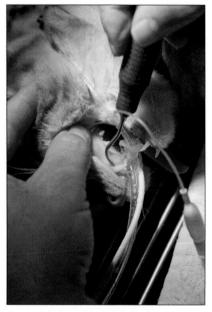

Figure 1-6: Regular professional cleanings keep your cat's teeth and gums healthy.
©iStock.com/f00sion

 You brush your own teeth regularly — probably at least twice a day — and still get regular check-ups with a dentist. Imagine what would happen if you never brushed your teeth or gave up your regular dental cleanings. Brushing daily is the ideal prevention for your cat. You can also do a number of other things at home to keep your cat's mouth in tip-top condition:

✔ Feed your cat a prescription or non-prescription dental diet.

✔ Let your cat play with dental treats and toys.

✔ Use dental rinses, gels, sprays, and so on.

Invest in some poultry-flavored cat dental paste and a kitty-friendly toothbrush and then follow these steps (the whole process takes about 40 seconds):

1. **Warm your cat up to the idea of having his teeth brushed by letting him lick some of the tooth-paste off the toothbrush.**

 Never use toothpaste made for people, which can be toxic to cats!

2. **Quickly move the brush to the back teeth on one side and then the other.**

 You need to brush only the outside of the teeth, next to your cat's cheeks. This is where the largest percentage of plaque is.

 If you don't remove plaque, it mineralizes and turns to tartar. Tartar cannot be removed with brushing. The constant plaque causes gingivitis, and periodontal disease can follow, resulting in pain (due to inflammation and infection) and eventually tooth loss. Studies suggest that a correlation exists between oral infection and diseases of the heart, liver, and kidneys. So schedule an annual dental appointment for your cat. Having the teeth cleaned annually (and treatment when indicated) keeps your pet healthy. After all, treating dental disease costs much more than prevention.

Taking care of your cat's coat

Cats stay pretty clean with no help from us humans — they often groom themselves all day long! Even so, your cat may enjoy a little help now and then, especially if he has long hair. Not only that, you can make these grooming sessions into a special time that deepens your connection.

You need a few things to keep your cat's fur clean and neat. Exactly what you purchase depends on your cat's coat type. Table 1-1 offers some guidance.

Table 1-1	Grooming Tools for Cats with Different Coats		
Tool	*Short Coat*	*Medium Coat*	*Long Coat*
Flea comb (with very narrowly spaced teeth)	X	X	
Fine-toothed comb (for clearing dead hair and small mats)	X	X	X
Medium- or coarse-toothed comb			X
Slicker brush (for applying finishing touches to a mat-free coat)	X	X	

Tool	Short Coat	Medium Coat	Long Coat
Pin brush (for finishing touches)			X
Detangling spray (for mats)			X

Make the grooming session enjoyable for your cat, not stressful (see Figure 1-7). Try brushing or combing your cat for a few minutes at first to see whether he likes it. Start extending the time as he becomes accustomed to the feel of the comb and brush. Some cats find the experience delightful and may even look forward to it!

Figure 1-7: Grooming can be enjoyable for a cat.
©iStock.com/RyersonClark

Here are examples of grooming regimens you may follow:

- ✔ **Cats with long, silky coats:** Cats like Persians and Himalayans, for example, ideally need daily brushing, combing, and detangling. They may even need an occasional bath or professional grooming.

    Long-haired cats with coats that don't mat quite so easily (the Maine Coon, for example) need less attention than the easily matted longhairs but more than the easy-care coats of the shorthairs.

- ✔ **Cats with medium or short coats:** These cats are fine with weekly grooming.

Grooming your cat regularly will help you notice any changes in your cat's coat, especially patches where hair is sparse or even missing. These patches could be signs of parasites, allergies, fungal infections, or even hormonal problems — all of which need to be checked out by your veterinarian.

Never try to cut mats out of your cat's fur. Doing so is dangerous and often leads to cutting your cat's skin, an injury that requires a trip to surgery to fix.

Trimming your cat's nails

Cats tend to take care of their nails themselves, as long as you give them a good scratching post. Still, you may find that you have to clip your cat's nails to keep them from getting too long and too sharp. To trim a cat's nails, you need nail clippers made for cats and a styptic pencil or styptic powder, to stop the bleeding in case you accidentally cut the nail too short.

If you have any concerns, ask your veterinarian to show you the best and safest way to clip your cat's nails.

 Don't make nail trimming an unpleasant experience for your cat. Start when he's still young (see Figure 1-8) and get him used to having his feet touched before you ever start to try using the clippers. Keep him calm with a lot of petting, loving, and maybe a few treats. If he starts to get upset, stop for the time being and come back later when he is quiet. The nails will still be there, and you will both be happier.

Figure 1-8: Start young to teach a cat not to mind having his nails trimmed.

Photograph by Weems S. Hutto, ©John Wiley & Sons, Inc.

Chapter 2

An Ounce of Prevention

. . . .

In This Chapter

▶ Relying on your vet for expert advice and help

▶ Ensuring that your cat is properly vaccinated

▶ Preventing and eliminating parasites

. . . .

*P*reventive care is easier on you, your cat, and your bank account than is treating a disease or condition that is impairing your cat's health or threatening her life. That's why you should take advantage of all the measures available today, starting with a thorough examination and continuing with vaccines and parasite control.

This chapter explains your vet's vital role in your cat's health, tells you what you can expect from routine veterinary visits, and outlines the feline vaccines available. You also find out how to protect your cat from parasites.

Understanding Your Vet's Role in Preventing Illness

The cornerstone of your cat's preventive-health regimen is an annual examination by your veterinarian. During this visit, your veterinarian, like the one in Figure 2-1, examines your cat from ear tip to tail tip, looking for anything that may signal a potential problem.

She ensures that your kitty gets the proper vaccines and offers expert advice on everything from behavior issues to parasite control. In addition to performing a thorough exam of your cat, your vet also asks you questions about your cat's habits and addresses any questions and concerns you may have about your cat's health.

Figure 2-1: Your veterinarian is a partner in your efforts to protect your cat's health.
©iStock.com/aabejon

Getting the Proper Vaccinations

Call them "shots" if you want, but vaccinations deserve a lot of respect for cutting the rates of infectious disease in cats. Before the introduction of vaccines, many cats were lost to diseases that are now often prevented completely or made significantly less severe. In fact, a series of vaccines for kittens and annual vaccines for cats are still believed to be one of the best ways to ensure good health for your cat.

Cats and vaccines

The ability to protect our furry friends from disease has come a long way in the last 10 to 20 years, and the development of excellent vaccines is no exception. Vaccines are necessary to protect against specific infectious diseases caused by viruses and bacteria, and generally the benefits outweigh any risks. Your veterinarian will be able to individualize a protocol based on your cat's needs, her lifestyle, and her risk of exposure (see Figure 2-2).

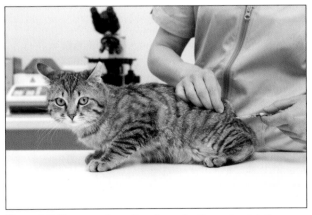

Figure 2-2: The many benefits of vaccination outweigh the few risks.

In general, vaccines work by stimulating your cat's immune system so that it can recognize a specific virus or bacteria in the vaccine and fight it off. In this way, vaccines protect your cat from future encounters with that disease-causing microbe by either preventing her from contracting the disease or lessening the disease's severity.

Core vaccines versus non-core vaccines

According to *Feline Preventive Healthcare Guidelines* (2011), published by the American Veterinary Medical Association (AVMA) and the American Animal Hospital Association (AAHA), and *AAFP Vaccination Guidelines* (2006), published by the American Association of Feline Practitioners (AAFP), there is a core group of diseases against which *all* cats should be vaccinated. The ones that are considered "non-core" vaccines are no less serious, but they may be regional or affect only certain populations of cats. Your veterinarian knows which diseases are common in your area and will design a protocol for your cat with this in mind. To read these guidelines, go to www.catvets.com and click on Feline Vaccination Advisory Panel Report.

Core vaccines

Following are the core vaccines:

✔ **Feline viral rhinotracheitis (also known as FHV-1, or Feline Herpes Virus):** FHV-1 (which is the *FVR* part of the FVRCP combination vaccine) is a herpes virus that causes severe upper respiratory problems in infected cats. Sneezing, runny eyes, nasal discharge, and sometimes sores in and around the mouth are the main things you will notice. Because FHV-1 is very contagious, all cats should receive this vaccine. The vaccine helps to reduce the severity and duration of the disease.

✓ **Calicivirus:** This virus (which constitutes the *C* in the FVRCP vaccine) has many strains. It is associated with upper respiratory disease in cats — what you might consider a cold. Cats with calicivirus have these symptoms: sneezing, discharge from the eyes and nose, and sometimes sores in the mouth. Calicivirus is highly contagious and spread through direct contact with infected cats. The vaccine helps to reduce the severity and the duration of the disease.

✓ **Panleukopenia:** Also known as *feline distemper,* (which is the *P* of the FVRCP vaccine), panleukopenia is a parvovirus specific to cats. It is highly infectious and often fatal, especially in unvaccinated kittens. Signs include vomiting, diarrhea, weakness, and a severe depression of the white blood cells. This highly contagious virus is very stable in the environment, which means it can hang around for a very long time.

✓ **Rabies:** This virus is found in the saliva and blood of animals and is commonly spread by a bite or by being exposed to secretions such as saliva. The virus is not specific to cats, meaning all rabies viruses are the same, whether they are in a dog, a raccoon, a cat, or a person. Because rabies is fatal and there is no treatment, most states and municipalities require rabies vaccines (either annually or every three years, depending on the vaccine) for *all* cats over 4 months old (whether they live inside or out).

Non-core vaccines

The non-core vaccines are

- ✔ **Feline leukemia virus (FeLV):** This is a type of virus known as a *retrovirus*. The virus attacks the immune system, making the cat more prone to becoming ill and sometimes causing tumors or leukemia. This highly infective agent is found in the saliva of cats, so any prolonged close contact that involves mutual grooming or even hissing can spread the virus.

- ✔ **Feline immunodeficiency virus (FIV):** This is the same family of viruses that causes HIV in people; however, this virus infects only cats (just as the human virus infects only people). It is also a retrovirus that significantly impairs the cat's immune system. The clinical signs are related to secondary infections, although severe gingivitis (inflammation of the gums) can often be associated with FIV. Compared to FeLV, this virus is not as contagious; it's mainly transmitted by bites, or it is transmitted in utero, from a mother cat to the fetus.

- ✔ **Feline infectious peritonitis (FIP):** This disease is caused by a coronavirus. Many cats have this virus in a *nonvirulent* form, meaning it doesn't cause disease. There is a *virulent* mutation, however, that is almost always fatal. The ability of the cat's immune system to fight off this virus may impact the level of disease. Cats in multi-cat households are at the highest risk for FIP, whereas most household pets are considered at low risk.

✔ **Chlamydia:** Chlamydia is caused by a bacterium, not a virus. The infective agent is *Chlamydophila felis,* which is found worldwide. It was originally thought to primarily cause upper respiratory disease in cats; however, the predominant clinical sign is conjunctivitis, an inflammation of the eye. There is commonly a discharge from the eyes that ranges from a clear fluid to a thick discharge containing both mucus and pus.

Getting Ticked Off at Parasites and Other Organisms

Cats pick up all kinds of parasites, both internal pests, such as worms, and external ones, such as fleas and ear mites. If parasites are present, your vet can prescribe medication to control or possibly eliminate them.

Parasites are more than a nuisance. They can also cause health problems like diarrhea and anemia, or transmit infectious diseases. Fortunately, most are easy to conquer, as this section explains.

Worms, worms, and more worms

In this section is all you ever want to know about worms: big worms, fat worms, mean worms, ugly worms — and even a worm that isn't really a worm but a kind of fungus (the ringworm). Read on for all the squirmy facts.

Heartworms

Heartworms have long been considered a dog owner's problem, but in the last 15 years, it has been recognized that cats and kittens can also be infected with this deadly parasite.

Heartworms are actual worms that are transmitted by common mosquitoes. After infecting a cat, the heartworm larvae migrate through the cat, eventually ending up in the lungs and occasionally the heart. Here are the answers to questions you may have about heartworms:

✔ **What signs should I look for?** Coughing is a relatively common sign and is often mistaken for hairballs or asthma. Other things you may see are vomiting, wheezing, difficulty breathing, lethargy, and weight loss.

 A single mosquito bite is enough to cause a potentially fatal illness. Sudden death without signs of disease has been reported in some cases.

✔ **Why should I protect my cat from heartworms?** The disease is very different in cats than it is in dogs:

- Unlike in dogs, heartworm in cats is very difficult to diagnose with a simple blood test.

- Most of the damage occurs in the *lungs* of the cat. In fact, to be harmful in cats, the heartworm does not need to grow to adult size, nor does it need to be in the heart. The heartworm larvae migrating in the cat can lead to a severe inflammatory response that causes irreversible lung damage known as *heartworm associated respiratory disease (HARD)*.

- Currently, there is no approved treatment for heartworms in cats as there is for dogs. Your veterinarian can't treat the adult heartworms in your cat because the medicine is toxic.

• Cats infected with heartworms are in potentially more danger than dogs are (and it's not pretty in dogs either!). Even one worm can present a serious reaction in a cat, sometimes presenting as respiratory collapse or sudden death.

REVOLUTION (selamectin): One treatment, many benefits

REVOLUTION (selamectin) is a safe, effective way to protect your cat or kitten from fleas, heartworms, hookworms, and roundworms. REVOLUTION is a topical solution that you apply to your cat's skin once a month.

To apply REVOLUTION, open the container, part the hair between your cat's shoulder blades, and apply the preventive directly to the skin, as shown here:

Photographs courtesy of Zoetis

Note: REVOLUTION is available only with a prescription from your veterinarian, so ask your pet's doctor whether it should be part of your monthly pet protection program.

• Indoor cats are not immune, because heart-worms can be carried inside by mosquitoes. In a clinical study, over 25 percent of cats diagnosed with adult heartworms were confirmed by their owners to be indoor-only cats.

 Currently, because no approved treatment for heartworm disease in cats exists, prevention is the best protection. Be sure to talk to your veterinarian about heartworm in your cat and see the nearby sidebar, "REVOLUTION (sela-mectin): One treatment, many benefits."

Tapeworms

Fleas tend to bring more than just themselves to the party on your cat's skin. They can also bring tape-worms. When a cat with fleas grooms herself, she may occasionally swallow a flea. If that flea happens to be carrying tapeworm eggs, it can lead to infection in the cat. (If instead of swallowing a flea, your cat happens to hunt and consume a mouse or other small rodent that is infected with tapeworms, the same thing happens; it's just a different type of tapeworm.)

After being ingested by the cat, the tapeworm eggs hatch, producing adult tapeworms that settle happily into her intestines, stealing nutrients. Usually, the tapeworms don't make the cat sick and are just hitch-hikers; however, a severe infection may result in weight loss, diarrhea, abdominal pain, and increased appetite.

 Sometimes, you can see the evidence of tape-worms in and around the base of your cat's tail. They look like dried white or yellow rice, although sometimes they may be moving around.

Your vet can prescribe medication that can treat the worms very effectively. Keep in mind, however, that these medications kill only those tapeworms that are currently in your cat; they don't prevent future infections.

 You can treat for tapeworms, but you'll never get rid of them until you get rid of the fleas. If the flea infestation is not eliminated, it is very possible for a cat to get infected repeatedly with tapeworms until the fleas are all gone.

Roundworms

Roundworms (also known as *ascarids*), are the most common internal parasite found in cats, and most cats will be infected at some time in their lives. Cat's become infected by picking up roundworm eggs in the dirt or grass, or by eating mice and other small mammals that are carrying worm larvae in their tissues. The worms live in the small intestine of the cat, and you may not even know it.

In a major infection, your cat may have a dull coat and a potbellied appearance. You may even see live worms in the vomit or the feces! Sometimes your cat may cough because the larvae migrate through the lungs as part of their life cycle.

 The best way to protect your cat against roundworms is to clean the litter pan daily, keep your cat inside to stop it from hunting, and deworm your cat on a regular basis. Your veterinarian can help you with roundworm diagnosis, treatment, and protection. See the sidebar "REVOLUTION (selamectin): One treatment, many benefits" for more information.

Hookworms

Hookworms are another common parasite that can live in a cat's intestines. They attach to the lining of the intestinal wall and feed on a cat's blood, passing eggs in the cat's feces.

Hookworm larvae hatch from the eggs that live in the soil and can infect your cat directly by penetrating through skin (through your cat's footpads or through the mucosa of her mouth). Cats and kittens can become infected by walking on infected soil or by using an infected litter box. Cats can also be infected by ingesting hookworms during routine grooming and when hunting and eating small rodents or even cockroaches that contain infective hookworm larvae. The larvae then grow in the small intestines where they attach and feed on blood.

 Hookworms are known to be voracious feeders. Cats that are infected with this parasite may show signs of anemia, diarrhea, and weight loss. Young kittens can easily die from the internal bleeding caused by hookworms.

 Your veterinarian can help you protect your kitten from hookworms. Head to the sidebar "REVOLUTION (selamectin): One treatment, many benefits" for information.

Ringworm

Despite its name, ringworm isn't a worm at all, but a fungus related to human athlete's foot. Ringworm causes hair loss in a circular pattern (see Figure 2-3). Unlike other parasites, the ringworm just stays on top of the skin and affects the hair and hair follicles.

The great news is that within two to four months of catching it, your cat should build up immunity to ringworm. Persians and Himalayans seem to be more susceptible than other breeds.

 Although *you* can use an over-the-counter fungal treatment, your cat can't. She'll just groom it off of her fur and get very sick in the process. There are many human medicines that are toxic to cats. Always consult with your vet about treatment.

 Make sure to wash your hands well after handling a kitty with ringworm to avoid getting ringworm yourself. If your cat has ringworm, wash her bedding with bleach and vacuum her favorite hangouts.

Figure 2-3: Ringworm, although contagious, isn't the end of the world.

Photography by Weems S. Hutto, ©John Wiley & Sons, Inc.

Itching to find out about fleas, ticks, and ear mites

Fleas, ticks, and ear mites are more than annoying — they can be a serious health risk. Persistence is the name of the game in controlling external parasites. The good news: Methods of controlling some of these pests have improved in the last decade and especially in the last couple of years.

Controlling fleas

Fleas are the most common external parasite found on cats. They feed on a cat's blood and lay eggs that fall off anywhere the cat spends her time, such as the carpet, the couch, or your bed. These eggs hatch and develop into adult fleas that can then re-infest pets in the home.

Fleas may also cause skin irritation or flea allergy dermatitis and can transmit other parasites, such as tapeworms and serious bacterial infections.

You may not be aware that your cat has fleas because cats are so meticulous about their grooming that they may remove the evidence. Some possible clues include the following:

- **You see your cat nibbling, licking, or scratching at her skin.** This is a signal that you should pull out the flea comb and see whether you can find any indication that fleas are living on your cat. If you're lucky (or unlucky), you may see a live flea running around in the her coat.

- **You see some tiny white and black specks that look like salt and pepper in your cat's coat.** The "pepper" is flea feces, sometimes called *flea dirt,* which is made up of blood. The "salt" is flea eggs.

TIP

To determine whether what you find is indeed flea feces, brush the dark specks onto a moistened piece of white paper towel. If the specks leave a red smear on the paper towel, they're flea dirt. If they don't leave a red smear, they're just plain old dirt.

If you discover that you have fleas in the house, you need a game plan for treating your pet and her environment. Not only must you kill the biting adult fleas (see Figure 2-4), but you must also keep developing fleas from reaching adulthood.

Here's a battle plan to help you get the infestation under control:

1. **Discuss with your veterinarian how to treat your cat (and any other pets you have) for fleas.**

   Your veterinarian and his veterinary team help people eliminate flea infestations all the

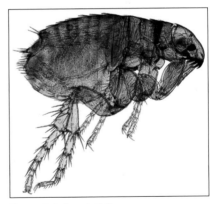

Figure 2-4: An adult flea.

©iStock.com/olikim

time. They can come up with the best plan by working with you.

The best and easiest way to keep fleas out of your house is with topical medication from the veterinarian. Discuss the options with your vet and see the earlier sidebar, "REVOLUTION (selamectin): One treatment, many benefits."

2. **Machine wash your cat's bedding (as well as the linens on your own bed) in hot soapy water.**

3. **Vacuum rugs, sofa cushions, drapes, and all floors, using a vacuum with a beater brush.**

   The vibration of the vacuum stimulates the fleas to hatch out of their pupa.

4. **Place the vacuum bag in a plastic bag and tape it shut so that no fleas jump out to re-infest your house.**

Be patient and persistent. Even if you do all of these things, it will take at least three months to fully rid your home of fleas. Therefore, stopping the fleas from ever invading your house is easier than cleaning up an infestation after it gets a foothold.

Eliminating ear mites

A small amount of wax in your cat's ears is perfectly normal. But if your pet's ears appear filthy and are very itchy, she may very well have ear mites — highly infectious little pests that feed on the lining of the ear canal (see Figure 2-5).

You need to see your veterinarian to be sure that you are indeed dealing with ear mites and, if so, to get

effective ther-
apy. Your vet-
erinarian can
verify the diag-
nosis by taking
a look at an
ear swab
under a micro-
scope, but the
black dis-
charge is usu-
ally a dead
giveaway. A
healthy ear
should be
clean and dry.

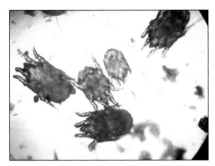

Figure 2-5: Ear mites live in your cat's ear canals.

©Agency-Animal-Picture/Getty Images

Not only do ear mites cause the inside of your kitty's head to itch around the clock, but they can eventually cause ear infections.

In addition, because ear mites are a social disease, if you have other pets, you need to treat everyone. Refer to the earlier sidebar, "REVOLUTION (selamectin): One treatment, many benefits." Ear mites can be really difficult to shake, so be persistent in your efforts to eradicate them.

Taking the bite out of ticks

If you allow your cat outside, one of the dangers she may face is picking up ticks in her rambles. She may dispense with them herself while grooming, but occasionally you'll find one of the bloodsucking beasties in a place your cat can't get to easily, such as at the base of her ear or her eyelids.

To remove a tick, use gloves and tweezers or a tick remover, and follow these steps:

1. **Grasp the tick's body firmly and pull with a steady motion.**

   If you pull slowly and straight out, the mouth should release. Don't twist the tick and don't use matches, cigarettes, or gasoline to remove the tick; he may just dig deeper.

    Don't worry if a piece of the imbedded head remains behind; it will work its way out in time and will not become infected.

2. **Kill the tick by placing it in alcohol; then flush it or throw it away.**

    You may want to save the dead tick in a resealable plastic bag, labeled with the date on which the tick was found. If your cat becomes ill, you can use the saved tick to identify the species that bit her, which can then help your veterinarian determine what is making her sick.

3. **Put a little antiseptic on the spot to prevent infection and keep an eye on the area until it's healed.**

4. **Wash your hands.**

    Ticks carry a lot of diseases that people can catch, including Lyme, Ehrlichiosis, and Rocky Mountain Spotted Fever, so be sure to wash your hands thoroughly after handling ticks.

    If your cat has a chronic problem with ticks, speak with your veterinarian about the safest way to keep your cat protected.

Chapter 3

Stress-Free Trips to the Vet? It Starts at Home

. . . .

In This Chapter

▶ Recognizing the need for routine veterinary care

▶ Socializing your cat

▶ Making car travel tolerable for your feline friend

▶ Dealing with motion sickness

. . . .

*Y*our feline friend doesn't need the power of speech to communicate to you just how much he dislikes going to the vet: If your experience is like many cat lovers', the complaining begins when you try to put him in his carrier, continues through the yowl-filled car ride and interminable wait in the reception area, and ends in stony silence in the examination room only because of the shock, *SHOCK*, of being touched and handled by a stranger! Back home, he may not speak to you for hours.

Fortunately, you can make these trips easier for your cat — and for yourself. Follow the suggestions in this chapter to change your cat's mindset from "Reasons I hate the vet" to "Well, if we *must.*"

Why Routine Veterinary Care Is a Must for Your Cat

Here's a sad fact: Many cats don't get the veterinary care they need. Some cat owners mistakenly believe that kitten immunizations are sufficient for a lifetime of protection (they aren't). Others believe that their cats, especially indoor cats, can't be exposed to dangerous diseases (they can). Even those who take their cats for immunizations may skip routine checkups, assuming that a sick cat will look sick (not necessarily).

There are two additional reasons why cats may not get the care they need: the expense of veterinary care and the difficulty of the trip itself. Head to the later section "A Car, a Crate, and a Cloth to Cover It With: Traveling with Kitty" in this chapter for suggestions on over-coming your cat's dislike of car rides, and go to Chapter 4 for information about health insurance and wellness plans for your pet.

Your inscrutable cat: Why ailments can go undetected

Without professional veterinary care, many feline ail-ments go undetected. Even if you diligently observe your cat and do the routine health checks at home that Chapter 1 recommends, you still may not recognize health problems in your cat. Read on to find out why.

Cats hide pain and illness very well

This trait probably evolved as a protective mechanism for life in the wild, but it's one reason that you may not be able to tell that your cat needs medical attention (see Figure 3-1).

Figure 3-1: Sick or just resting? It may be hard to tell because cats hide pain and illness.

Your seriously ill cat may not show any signs

A cat can have heart disease for years, for example, before any symptoms appear, and some cats may never display clinical signs that would alert you to seek medical care. Similarly, some cats who are exposed to the feline leukemia virus (FeLV; see Chapter 2) may show mild symptoms or no symptoms, even though they have been infected. Only through routine veterinary care and regular health checks can these "hidden" conditions be discovered and treated.

Some conditions present differently than you expect

When you observe your cat for signs of illness, you may watch for symptoms that you're familiar with. However, some conditions present with symptoms other than the ones you think to look for. Take arthritis, for example. A cat with arthritis may slow down, become irritable, and stop going to the litter box because it hurts to get in or to squat down — symptoms you may attribute to simply aging or to behavior problems.

Heartworm infection is another example. Most people associate heartworms with dogs and assume that the signs of heartworms in cats are similar and progress in the same way: tiring easily, coughing, losing weight, and difficulty exercising. Yet your cat's cough may be due to heartworm infection rather than spitting up hairballs. (Head to Chapter 2 for details on heartworm in cats.)

Giving special care for older cats

Cats age more quickly than do people, and they enter their senior years around age 10. As cats age, they slow down a bit, sleep a bit more, and are at increased risk of developing chronic conditions, such as diabetes and arthritis, and serious illnesses, like cancer and kidney disease. As a result, older cats often benefit from even more frequent checkups.

Why even indoor cats need routine veterinary care

Given that many of the feline infectious diseases spread through contact with other cats or contaminated environments (refer to Chapter 2), owners of indoor cats may mistakenly assume that their cats don't need to be immunized and can forego routine veterinary care altogether. Although living indoors does protect your cat in many ways — reducing the likelihood that he will be exposed to certain infectious diseases or be injured — regular veterinary care is still necessary.

First, consider that your indoor can get out, and mosquitos, fleas, and other parasites can get in. You, your dog, other outdoor cats, or your family may inadvertently bring in unwanted parasites. Also remember that rabies vaccinations are mandatory in many states and that some of the infectious diseases that plague cats can linger in an environment for years (refer to Chapter 2), meaning that you may not even be aware that your cat has been exposed.

Second, living indoors brings its own health issues that stem from a restricted environment (see Figure 3-2), a usually sedentary life, and perpetually available kibble. These factors can lead to both behavior and health problems, such as feline anxiety and obesity.

Figure 3-2: Indoor cats have their own health issues that bene-fit from veterinary care.

©iStock.com/Joe_Potato

Socializing Your Cat to New People and Places

There's a certain period during a cat's life when he learns how to interact with other creatures — feline, human, and other animals — and grows accustomed to the sights, smells, and noises in his environment. In essence, he learns what's normal. These early impressions are important because they affect how well he will be able to tolerate unfamiliar people, animals, and events as an adult cat.

Starting when Kitty is young

A cat is most receptive to socialization between 2 and 7 weeks old. During this time, you can help him grow into a well-adjusted adult cat by carefully exposing him to people, places, and noises that he'll encounter throughout his life. Here are some suggestions:

- **Make sure your kitten is handled by people.** Being gently handled by people of all ages teaches your cat that he doesn't have to fear and can actually enjoy human companionship (see Figure 3-3). Doing so will also help him during future interactions with his veterinarian because he will have learned that being touched, held, and moved around is not, in itself, threatening.

- **Foster pleasant interactions with other animals.** If possible, help him make friends with the canines in your own family — or with any other cooperative and friendly dogs.

- **Introduce him to new experiences.** Your cat doesn't need to spend a year backpacking through Europe, but he shouldn't think the only safe place is home, either. Take him to places where he can meet new people, see new surroundings, and play with different toys (be sure he's been properly vaccinated first). This not only helps him learn proper social skills, but if you travel to these places by car, you also teach him that car rides can take him to places he enjoys.

Figure 3-3: During socialization, your kitten learns to enjoy being touched and spending time around people.
©iStock.com/FrankyDeMeyer

 Kitten socialization classes are a growing trend. Ask your veterinarian about classes that may be available in your area.

By taking the time to socialize your cat when he is young, you help him grow into a confident, well-adjusted companion, one who will likely continue to remain on good terms with all the people, animals, and experiences — including those he encounters in the veterinary clinic — throughout his life.

What you can do for an older cat

The ideal socialization period occurs when a cat is between the ages of 2 and 7 weeks old. After that time, his perceptions of the world become hardwired and very difficult to change. But don't give up. Even cats who missed out on early socialization can learn to be more comfortable around strange people, animals, and places, but it will take time and patience.

Be aware, however, that highly anxious cats who did not receive proper socialization may never completely overcome their fears. In this situation, your goal is to eliminate as many stressors as you can.

A Car, a Crate, and a Cloth to Cover It With: Traveling with Kitty

For many cats, the worst part of any trip is the car ride itself. The movement, the noise, and — if he only rides in a car for his trips to the vet — the destination all create a stew of negative associations. You can neutralize some of the most potent of these negative associations by making the car ride, at least tolerable. This section tells you how.

Your cat's carrier: His happy place

A cat carrier, or crate, is a wonderful item to have. It functions as a car seat during car trips and a home away from home in strange places. If you can get your cat to love his crate (see Figure 3-4), you'll have taken the most important step toward making trips to the vet less stressful and more — dare we say it? — tolerable.

Figure 3-4: A carrier can be your cat's happy place.
©iStock.com/g215

Choosing a crate that's cat- and vet-friendly

A cat carrier is a must-have item when you're taking your cat to the vet. Look for a carrier that has adequate ventilation and is large enough for your cat to recline comfortably but small enough that you can carry it easily. A top that opens or that can be completely removed is also helpful if your cat is especially anxious. These carriers enable the veterinarian to conduct at least part of the examination with the cat still in the carrier.

Acclimating your cat to his crate

Your cat's carrier is the safest way for him to travel, but if the only time he sees his carrier is right before you stuff him into it for his trip to the veterinarian, he's going to resist — sometimes vehemently. The trick is to teach him to like his crate.

To help your cat learn to like his carrier, try these suggestions:

- ✔ **Treat the carrier like a piece of furniture in your house.** Put it in a room your cat spends time in and leave it there so that he can explore it in his own good time. Be sure to leave the carrier door open to encourage his exploring the inside, too.

- ✔ **Make the carrier enticing.** Put something familiar to your cat in the carrier: a favorite toy, the sock he likes to carry around, comfy bedding — preferably things that smell like him, you, or your house.

- ✔ **Let your cat explore the carrier *on his own*.** Don't force him to look at it. Don't put him in it. Let him get into and out of the carrier at will (see Figure 3-5).

 You can encourage his going into the crate by teasing him with a cat toy through the air openings. Make sure you let him leave when he's ready, though.

The carrier isn't just a comfy den/play area, however. It's also your cat's transport vehicle, so after he's comfortable with the carrier itself, help him learn to be comfortable — or at least not panicky — when you use it to transport him around:

- ✔ **When you see your cat lounging comfortably in his carrier, close the door for a few seconds, praise him, and give him a treat.** As he grows more accustomed to the closed door, extend the time.

- ✔ **Practice lifting the carrier up, with your cat inside, and carrying it around the house.** This helps him get accustomed to the movement.

The next step is to teach your cat to tolerate car rides. Once he's comfortable in the carrier, that task becomes a whole lot easier.

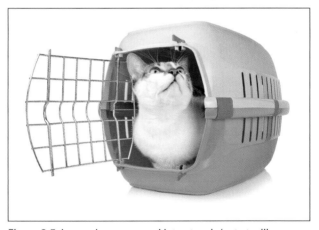

Figure 3-5: Leave door open and let cat go in/out at will.
©iStock.com/sergoua

Cruising can be fun: Teaching your cat to enjoy the ride

A cat who is comfortable in his carrier is much better able to tolerate car rides because his carrier is his transport within a transport (see Figure 3-6). Here are some suggestions to ensure a safe and relatively peaceful ride:

- **Secure the carrier in the car.** Several are designed to work with a car's seatbelts or come with the necessary adapters. If your carrier doesn't have special seatbelt loops, run the seatbelt through the handle.

- **Practice, practice, practice.** Practice taking the carrier out to the car. Practice turning on the car (so that your cat can get used to the sounds of the engine). Practice driving around with your cat in the car, starting with very short trips — even just down to the end of the driveway or around the block — and going farther afield as your cat gets more accustomed to the sensations.

- **Routinely take your cat for a ride and go to a variety of places.** The more normal car rides become, the less stressful they are for your cat. What you don't want to do is fall into the habit of using the carrier only for veterinary visits, which will undo all the good work you've already done.

- **If your cat continues to fear car rides, cover the crate with a towel or small blanket while it is in the car.** Doing so can help block out the noises and sights that may be frightening him.

These strategies teach your cat that car rides are just part of his life and not something to fear. Even if your cat never embraces life as world traveler, these tricks may help him better tolerate the trips he has to take.

Figure 3-6: Your cat should be in his carrier whenever he travels in a car.

©iStock.com/Vasiliki Varvaki

 Even cats that get along very well can become aggressive toward each other when they are stressed. To avoid this situation, consider using separate carriers for car rides if you have multiple cats.

Green around the Gills: Overcoming Carsickness

Some cats, like some people, get carsick. In cats, the main cause of motion sickness is stress and anxiety. This section explains how to recognize motion sickness in your cat and tells you what you can do about it.

One of the first signs of motion sickness in a cat is one that's easy to misinterpret: the incessant meowing and howling that you may think is just his way of telling you how displeased he is. Other signs include drooling, panting, restlessness or pacing, lethargy or withdrawal, vomiting, and diarrhea.

The first line of defense is to reduce the anxiety your cat experiences when traveling. Refer to the earlier section "A Car, a Crate, and a Cloth to Cover It With: Traveling with Kitty" to find out how you can make the car trip better, and go to Chapter 4 for strategies you can use at the vet's office to ease his anxiety there.

 Beyond these strategies, you can do the following to reduce your cat's distress:

- Withhold food three to four hours before traveling. An empty stomach reduces nausea.

- Keep the car cool and quiet. Use the car's cooling system rather than open the windows (which lets in blowing air and noise).

- Prepare for an accident. Use puppy pads or place a thick layer of wadded up paper towels on the floor of the carrier in the event that your nervous cat has a bout of diarrhea or vomits.

 If the preceding suggestions don't alleviate the problem, ask your veterinarian about herbal remedies or medication designed to alleviate your cat's anxiety or the symptoms of motion sickness.

Chapter 4

At the Vet: Making Your Cat Glad She Came

. . . .

In This Chapter

▶ Making the veterinary visit less stressful

▶ Creating a checklist for yourself beforehand

▶ Looking at pet insurance and wellness plans

. . . .

*E*ven though more people have cats than dogs as pets, dogs far outnumber cats in visits for routine veterinary care. One of the reasons for this discrepancy? Cat owners' reluctance to make their cats do something that they so obviously dislike. For animals that prefer predictability and being in control, veterinary visits can be very difficult for cats. The strange animals and people, the unfamiliar environment, and — let's face it — the examination itself can be very stressful for your cat. Yet with a few helpful strategies, you can reduce your cat's anxiety during these visits, as this chapter explains.

Relieving Stress — Yours and Your Cat's — at the Vet

Historically, cats have had a reputation as solitary animals who are aloof, territorial, and protective of their spaces; who dislike and will avoid interaction with other animals; and who, when forced to endure companions — feline, canine, or human — do so only reluctantly and only for self-serving purposes.

More recent research into feline behavior and social systems, however, paints a much more interesting and complex picture. Cats *are* social and often form very tight and long-lasting bonds with the other animals and humans in their group. In other words, your cat loves you, her home, and her daily routine. She loves the familiar scents and the comfy window seat and — when he's not doing something foolish — she loves the dog. What she doesn't love is unpredictability, unfamiliar things, and not being in control.

A trip to the vet condenses all the things a cat doesn't love into one anxiety-producing field trip. First, she has to wait in a room full of strange, noisy, often fearful animals. Then she's taken into a tiny room and placed on a cold, slippery table where a stranger who smells like soap, chemicals, and other animals touches her all over, sticks a cold glass thermometer up her rear end, and pokes her with at least one needle, often more.

With all these easy-for-a-cat-to-dislike experiences occurring simultaneously, you may never be able to teach your cat to love trips to the veterinarian, but you *can* make those trips much easier on her.

Hanging out in the waiting room

The noise, the smells, the unpredictable (to a cat) activity all around her, and the inability to escape all make time spent in the waiting room an assault on an anxious cat's senses. Follow the suggestions in this section to make the wait less nerve-racking.

Cats that are anxious or frightened may tremble, withdraw, or exhibit passive escape behaviors, such as going very still or hiding. Other characteristics that may indicate your cat is stressed include a puffed tail that's held low (or perhaps even tucked under) and flattened ears (see Figure 4-1).

Figure 4-1: Fearful or anxious cats let you know through their demeanor and body position.

©iStock.com/Vampirica

Keep her in her crate

The first and best thing you can do to ease your cat's anxiety during a trip to the veterinary clinic is to take her in her cat carrier or crate. Tucked safely inside, your cat will be shielded from a lot of what causes her stress.

Here are some other suggestions:

- ✔ **Ensure that the crate smells like your cat and home.** If the crate is always out in your home and your cat is allowed to go into and out of it at will, then you're good. Otherwise, you can make the crate feel more familiar: Before leaving home, gently rub a soft cloth over your cat's face and then run the cloth around the inside of the carrier. Toss the cloth and a couple of smell-good items — a favorite toy, a cushion from her bed — into the crate.

- ✔ **Elevate the crate.** What does your cat do when she wants to get away from people and activity that she doesn't like? She gets up high. Help her out as much as you can in the waiting room: Put the crate on a chair rather than on the floor (see Figure 4-2).

- ✔ **Cover the crate with a cloth or turn it toward you.** Sometimes, out of sight is out of mind. Hide her from the chaos by draping a cloth or towel over the crate or turning the crate so that its door faces you.

Head to Chapter 3 for more tips on how to turn your cat's carrier into a haven during trips.

Figure 4-2: Keep the carrier elevated.
©iStock.com/pixelprof

Other strategies to ease her fears during the wait

Here are a couple of other strategies you can use to ease your cat's wait:

- ✔ **If possible, find a quiet place to wait.** Steer clear of other animals (especially dogs who are likely to want to come up for a friendly sniff) and small children (who are likely to want to see and pet your kitty).

- ✔ **Schedule your visit during the vet's slow periods.** Less noise and fewer animals makes for a less stressful visit. Ask your veterinarian whether the clinic has special days when it sees only cats.

In the examination room

In the examination room, take things slowly and let your cat determine when is the best time to venture from her carrier. Ask your veterinarian whether it's okay to let your cat explore the exam room, but be aware of any places where she can hide.

If she is particularly skittish or if the examination room has places where she can hide, leave her in the crate while you wait for the veterinarian, who is an expert on handling cats and knows how to make the examination as low-stress as possible. In fact, you'll probably notice that the veterinarian does things specifically intended to relieve your cat's stress, such as letting her sniff things like the stethoscope (see Figure 4-3).

Veterinarians can tell a lot about the health of an animal from the way it moves and looks, so don't be surprised if your vet doesn't immediately begin the hands-on portion of his examination of your cat. In fact, as Fluffy sniffs around the room, the veterinarian will likely want to chat with you about her habits and behaviors, health concerns you may have, and so on. This time spent talking accomplishes a couple of important things: In addition to giving you a chance to share any concerns or information about your cat with your vet, it also gives your cat the opportunity to become accustomed to your vet's presence, which makes the actual hands-on part of the exam much less stressful.

Hop over to the later section "Getting the Most from the Visit: A Guide for Pet Parents" for advice and strategies on how to ensure you're ready with the information your vet will want to know.

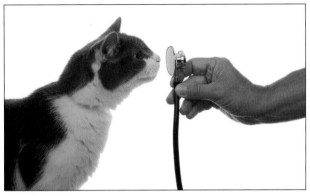

Figure 4-3: Letting your cat sniff around can help alleviate her stress.

©iStock.com/hanzl

Back home again

After a visit to the veterinary clinic, your cat will bring home a variety of unfamiliar scents. These scents will be even more pronounced if her stay was a prolonged one — she had to stay overnight, for example — and can cause anxiety in other cats you may have at home. To lessen the anxiety felt all around, follow these suggestions:

✔ **Place the carrier in its usual place and open the door so that your cat can come out when she chooses.** And then leave her alone to decide on her own when is the right time to re-emerge.

- ✔ **Separate the returning cat from the others for a little while.** This gives her a chance to pick up the familiar scents of your home. Also, stay close-by to monitor the interactions.

 The unfamiliar smells won't necessarily stress out your dog, but he will be curious and will follow your cat around, sniffing her fur. Make sure that she can get away from him, or, better yet, keep them separated until she feels — and smells — more like herself.

- ✔ **Spread the scents around.** Gently rub the faces of your kitties with the same soft-cloth. Doing so mixes up all the scents, camouflaging the unfamiliar with the familiar. You can also switch their bedding around.

- ✔ **If your cat was at the clinic for a prolonged stay, wash any bedding or toys that stayed with her.** Doing so removes the clinic smell.

Getting the Most from the Visit: A Guide for Pet Parents

Your veterinarian sees himself as your partner. His goal is to help you maintain and improve your cat's health. Just as he will ask you questions during your cat's visit to the clinic, he also anticipates that you'll have questions for him. To ensure that you each get the information you need to make the best healthcare decisions for your cat, take a little time to prepare before the visit.

Prepping beforehand

Before your veterinary appointment, make notes of changes in your cat's health or behavior. In your notes include

- ✔ Your cat's diet (type and amount of food) and any changes you've observed

- ✔ Any changes in your cat's bathroom habits

- ✔ Any changes in your cat's activity and energy levels

- ✔ Any medications or supplements you are giving her, whether you got them from the vet or some other source, and her response to them

- ✔ Any health concerns you may have (note when you first noticed the problem and how it has changed or progressed)

- ✔ Any other questions you may have

Write these things down so that you don't forget any important information. These notes also ensure that you can provide the veterinarian with the information he needs to conduct a thorough examination and ensure that you don't forget to ask any of your questions.

Exploring Pet Insurance and Wellness Plans

If your cat gets sick, her medical bills can grow rapidly. Buying pet insurance or enrolling in a wellness plan may be a way that you can manage your pet's medical expenses. If you are interested in either of these types of plans, discuss your options with someone on the veterinary team.

Building a long-term relationship with your vet

The relationship you have with your cat's veterinarian and the entire healthcare team is a critical factor in her health and longevity, so nourish that relationship. Take her by the office just to say "hi" and send in pictures of your kitten as she grows and throughout her life. Someone on the veterinary team will proudly post those pictures on the clinic's a bulletin board — after all, your vet and the other members of the veterinary team work to promote the health of pets like yours every day.

Understanding how pet insurance works

The premise of health insurance for pets is pretty much the same as insurance for humans. You pay an annual or monthly premium and, if your pet needs medical treatment that's covered by your policy, the insurance pays a percentage of the costs.

Certainly, having pet health insurance can eliminate the sticker shock and give you more options if your pet requires intensive treatments. If you decide to purchase healthcare insurance for your cat, be sure to find out the following before you settle on any one plan:

- **What medical care the policy covers:** If you're buying only emergency care, for example, make sure you understand what conditions qualify as an emergency under your coverage (see Figure 4-4).

✔ **How much of the bill is covered:** Most pet health-care plans pay for a percentage of the final cost. Be sure you know what percentage your plan pays.

✔ **How to make claims:** Does the insurance company expect you to pay the veterinary bill in full and then submit paperwork for reimbursement, or does the veterinary office file the claim for reimbursement and then bill you the remainder?

✔ **Whether a multi-pet discount is available:** If you insure more than one pet, many companies give you a discount.

Figure 4-4: Know what procedures and services your insurance or wellness plan covers.

©iStock.com/webphotographeer

Looking into wellness plans

Some veterinary practices and insurance companies offer wellness plans that cover routine vet visits, vaccinations, and so on. In these plans, you pay a monthly fee and in return receive discounts on routine and preventive healthcare. These plans may cover annual checkups, vaccinations, and routine health checks (fecal exams, deworming, and heartworm checks, for example), and they may offer discounts on other services and on medications. With such programs, you can spread out (and perhaps reduce) the costs of routine veterinary care.

Keep in mind, however, that these plans often include exclusions (they may not cover hereditary diseases, pre-existing conditions, or catastrophic illness, for example), and there may be restrictions on where you can access the plan's services (often limited to a particular practice or a network of practices).

Chapter 5

Ten Ways to Keep Your Cat Healthy

. . . .

In This Chapter

▶ Keeping your cat safe at home

▶ Teaming up with your vet for regular checkups and vaccines

▶ Understanding the benefits of spaying and neutering

. . . .

*T*his book is chock-full of information on cat care and how you can partner with your veterinary team to help ensure that your cat enjoys a long, healthy life. Of all the things you can do, however, the most important advice can be boiled down to the ten suggestions in this chapter.

Get Your Cat Vaccinated

Cats are vulnerable to a number of horrible, life-threatening diseases: feline immunodeficiency virus (FIV), feline leukemia virus (FeLV), feline infectious peritonitis (FIP), and rabies. All of these are contagious, spread from cat to cat, and are potentially deadly. They are all also preventable — if you get your cat vaccinated.

Begin your cat's vaccination regimen when he is a kitten and continue with boosters as needed throughout the rest of his life. Chapter 2 tells you what you need to know about vaccinations available for cats.

Visit the Vet Regularly

You and your cat's vet form the team that keeps him healthy. Going to the veterinarian regularly for routine checkups and vaccinations is one of the most important things you can do for your cat's health and well-being.

Plan on taking your cat to the vet for a routine physical examination at least once a year. (During their first year, kittens go more frequently.) During this visit, your vet will examine your cat, test for parasites, check for signs of viruses or infections, and give you helpful information and updates about your cat's health.

Feed Your Cat Right

To make sure your kitty's eating right, follow these simple guidelines and consult with your veterinarian about the best food for her:

- ✔ **Choose foods that are appropriate for your cat's age.** Adult and older cats can do just fine on regular adult cat food, but kittens need more fat and protein and should be fed products designed for them.

- ✔ **Choose foods with the AAFCO (Association of American Feed Control Officials) statement.** Whether you buy your cat's food from the supermarket, a pet-supply store, or your veterinarian, as long as you're dealing with a food that meets the nutritional levels established by the AAFCO pet food nutrient profiles, you should be fine.

Premium cat foods often contain higher-quality, more digestible ingredients, which means that the cat uses more of the food and may ultimately deposit less in the litter box.

Spay or Neuter Your Cat

Spaying your female cat can help prevent feline breast cancers, the most common cancer found among female cats. It can also help prevent a number of diseases that are related to reproduction, such as ovarian and uterine cancers, and infections such as *pyometra* (infection of the uterus). In males, neutering prevents prostate enlargement and can reduce the occurrences of anal and rectal tumors.

Take Care of Your Cat's Teeth

If you don't clean your cat's teeth regularly, plaque will develop. Without proper dental care, the plaque will mineralize and turn to tartar. When tartar forms, periodontal disease and gingivitis follow, leaving infection, pain, and missing teeth in their wake. Worse still, a correlation exists between oral infection and diseases of the heart, liver, and kidneys. So brush your cat's teeth regularly (Chapter 1 tells you how) and schedule an annual dental appointment for your cat to maintain proper dental health.

Consider Keeping Your Cat Indoors

A lot of dangers exist for cats that are left to roam out-doors, and indoor cats are at lower risk of contracting the diseases that threaten felines: rabies, FeLV, FIV, and FIP. Outdoor cats can be involved in fights, attacked, or hit by cars.

 If you have declawed your cat, you must keep him inside. Without claws, he's less able to defend himself against dogs and other dangers, and he'll have a harder time climbing to safety if attacked.

Protect Your Cat from High Falls

So many cats (especially young cats) jump or fall from open windows that the phenomenon even has a name: *high-rise syndrome.* You can keep your cat safe from such falls by doing the following:

- ✔ Regularly checking to see that your screens are in good shape and secure
- ✔ Keeping your windows closed when you aren't home
- ✔ Never leaving your cat unattended on a balcony

Keep Your Cat at a Good Weight

Obesity is the top nutrition-related problem in cats. In fact, up to four out of ten cats show up at their veterinarian's office carrying too much weight. An overweight cat is prone to a host of related problems, including diabetes; joint, ligament, and tendon problems; breathing problems; and even skin problems in exceptionally fat cats who can't groom themselves correctly.

 To prevent your cat from gaining excess weight, you need to give him the correct amount of food. Your vet can guide you on how much is too much.

Pay Attention to Signs of Ill Health

No one knows your cat better than you do. Use that knowledge to stay alert to signs that something is amiss, and at least once a month, turn one of your petting sessions into a mini-exam. As you run your hands over your cat's body, feel for lumps, bumps, and other abnormalities or changes. While you're at it, do a bit of grooming: trim his nails, check and clean his teeth, and so on. These friendly little checkups are the best way to stay in touch with your cat's health status. Chapter 1 has the details.

Remove Poisonous Plants from Your Home

Most cats chew on plants to pass the time, and a number of houseplants are toxic to cats; some — like many of the most popular flowers — can even be deadly to felines.

To protect your cat, replace toxic plants with safe alternatives. Talk with your vet about which varieties are problems and which are safe. For a complete list of toxic and nontoxic plants, go to http://www.aspca.org.

Make Your Cat Trackable

Okay, so this tip isn't really a health issue, but it's important for your cat's well-being nonetheless. To ensure that your cat can be returned safely home in the event that he gets lost, outfit him with a breakaway or safety collar (one designed to release with pressure and thus prevent accidental choking) and tags, or a microchip. Cat collars are an inexpensive insurance against loss, and the ID (either a tag or a microchip) gives your cat a ticket home.

Protection is a first priority

It's important to have the basics covered—a warm home, a healthy diet and lots of love. But protecting your new kitten from harmful parasites should be a top priority.

REVOLUTION® (selamectin) is the #1 choice for veterinarians when it comes to protecting cats against fleas, heartworms, roundworms[*], hookworms[†] and ear mites.[1]

Go to **puppykittenrewards.com** to receive a coupon for free doses of REVOLUTION. You'll get **3 FREE doses when you buy 9** or 2 free doses when you buy 6. And you can download even more tips.

 Litter training

 What to feed your kitten

 Stop your cat from scratching furniture

[*] *Toxocara cati* [†] *Ancylostoma tubaeforme*

Sign up for rewards, reminders and more tips at puppykittenrewards.com

IMPORTANT SAFETY INFORMATION: Do not use REVOLUTION on sick, weak, or underweight cats. Use only on cats 8 weeks and older. Side effects may include digestive upset and temporary hair loss at application site with possible inflammation. In people, REVOLUTION may be irritating to skin and eyes. Wash hands after use. See full Prescribing Information on page 73.

VetInsite™ Analytics 2014. Zoetis Data on File.

zoetis

Want even more tips and advice?

Go to puppykittenrewards.com

$ Download coupon for free doses

🐾 Sign up for reminders

🖥 View, download and print tips on training, nutrition, grooming and lifetime care

NADA 141-152, Approved by FDA

REVOLUTION® (selamectin)
Topical Parasiticide For Dogs and Cats

CAUTION:
US Federal law restricts this drug to use by or on the order of a licensed veterinarian.

DESCRIPTION:
Revolution (selamectin) Topical Parasiticide is available as a colorless to yellow, ready to use solution in single dose tubes for topical (dermal) treatment of dogs six weeks of age and older and cats eight weeks of age and older. The content of each tube is formulated to provide a minimum of 2.7 mg/lb (6 mg/kg) of body weight of selamectin. The chemical composition of selamectin is (5Z,25S)-25-cyclohexyl-4′-O-de(2,6-dideoxy-3-O-methyl-α-L-$arabino$-hexopyranosyl)-5-demethoxy-25-de (1-methylpropyl)-22,23-dihydro-5-hydroxyiminoavermectin A$_{1a}$.

INDICATIONS:
Revolution is recommended for use in dogs six weeks of age or older and cats eight weeks of age and older for the following parasites and indications:

Dogs:
Revolution kills adult fleas and prevents flea eggs from hatching for one month and is indicated for the prevention and control of flea infestations *(Ctenocephalides felis)*, prevention of heartworm disease caused by *Dirofilaria immitis*, and the treatment and control of ear mite *(Otodectes cynotis)* infestations. Revolution also is indicated for the treatment and control of sarcoptic mange *(Sarcoptes scabiei)* and for the control of tick infestations due to *Dermacentor variabilis*.

Cats:
Revolution kills adult fleas and prevents flea eggs from hatching for one month and is indicated for the prevention and control of flea infestations *(Ctenocephalides felis)*, prevention of heartworm disease caused by *Dirofilaria immitis*, and the treatment and control of ear mite *(Otodectes cynotis)* infestations. Revolution is also indicated for the treatment and control of roundworm *(Toxocara cati)* and intestinal hookworm *(Ancylostoma tubaeforme)* infections in cats.

WARNINGS:
Not for human use. Keep out of the reach of children.
In humans, Revolution may be irritating to skin and eyes. Reactions such as hives, itching and skin redness have been reported in humans in rare instances. Individuals with known hypersensitivity to Revolution should use the product with caution or consult a health care professional. Revolution contains isopropyl alcohol and the preservative butylated hydroxytoluene (BHT). Wash hands after use and wash off any product in contact with the skin immediately with soap and water. If contact with eyes occurs, then flush eyes copiously with water. In case of ingestion by a human, contact a physician immediately. The material safety data sheet (MSDS) provides more detailed occupational safety information. For a copy of the MSDS or to report adverse reactions attributable to exposure to this product, call 1-888-963-8471.

Flammable - Keep away from heat, sparks, open flames or other sources of ignition.

Do not use in sick, debilitated or underweight animals (see SAFETY).

PRECAUTIONS:
Prior to administration of Revolution, dogs should be tested for existing heartworm infections. At the discretion of the veterinarian, infected dogs should be treated to remove adult heartworms. Revolution is not effective against adult *D. immitis* and, while the number of circulating microfilariae may decrease following treatment, Revolution is not effective for microfilariae clearance.

Hypersensitivity reactions have not been observed in dogs with patent heartworm infections administered three times the recommended dose of Revolution. Higher doses were not tested.

ADVERSE REACTIONS:
Pre-approval clinical trials:
Following treatment with Revolution, transient localized alopecia with or without inflammation at or near the site of application was observed in approximately 1% of 691 treated cats. Other signs observed rarely (≤0.5% of 1743 treated cats and dogs) included vomiting, loose stool or diarrhea with or without blood, anorexia, lethargy, salivation, tachypnea, and muscle tremors.
Post-approval experience:
In addition to the aforementioned clinical signs that were reported in pre-approval clinical trials, there have been reports of pruritus, urticaria, erythema, ataxia, fever, and rare reports of death. There have also been rare reports of seizures in dogs (see **WARNINGS**).

DOSAGE:
The recommended minimum dose is 2.7 mg selamectin per pound (6 mg/kg) of body weight.

Administer the entire contents of a single dose tube (or two tubes used in combination for dogs weighing over 130 pounds) of Revolution topically in accordance with the following tables. (See **ADMINISTRATION** for the recommended treatment intervals.)

Cats (lb)	Package color	mg per tube	Potency (mg/mL)	Administered volume (mL)
Up to 5	Mauve	15 mg	60	0.25
5.1–15	Blue	45 mg	60	0.75
15.1–22	Taupe	60 mg	60	1.0

For cats over 22 lbs use the appropriate combination of tubes.

Dogs (lb)	Package color	mg per tube	Potency (mg/mL)	Administered volume (mL)
Up to 5	Mauve	15 mg	60	0.25
5.1–10	Purple	30 mg	120	0.25
10.1–20	Brown	60 mg	120	0.5
20.1–40	Red	120 mg	120	1.0
40.1–85	Teal	240 mg	120	2.0
85.1–130	Plum	360 mg	120	3.0

For dogs over 130 lbs use the appropriate combination of tubes.
Recommended for use in dogs 6 weeks of age and older and in cats 8 weeks of age and older.

ADMINISTRATION:
A veterinarian or veterinary technician should demonstrate or instruct the pet owner regarding the appropriate technique for applying Revolution topically to dogs and cats prior to first use.
Firmly press the cap down to puncture the seal on the Revolution tube; a clicking sound will confirm that the cap has successfully punctured the seal. Remove the cap and check to ensure that the tip of the tube is open. To administer the product, part the hair on the back of the animal at the base of the neck in front of the shoulder blades until the skin is visible. Place the tip of the tube on the skin and squeeze the tube 3 or 4 times to empty its entire contents directly onto the skin in one spot. Keeping the tube squeezed, drag it away from the liquid and lift to remove. Check the tube to ensure that it is empty. Do not massage the product into the skin. Due to alcohol content, do not apply to broken skin. Avoid contact between the product and fingers. Do not apply when the haircoat is wet. Bathing or shampooing the dog 2 or more hours after treatment will not reduce the effectiveness of Revolution against fleas or heartworm. Bathing or shampooing the cat 2 hours after treatment will not reduce the effectiveness of Revolution against fleas. Bathing or shampooing the cat 24 hours after treatment will not reduce the effectiveness of Revolution against heartworm. Stiff hair, clumping of hair, hair discoloration, or a slight powdery residue may be observed at the treatment site in some animals. These effects are temporary and do not affect the safety or effectiveness of the product. Discard empty tubes in your ordinary household refuse.